THE VALUE OF
CURIOSITY
13
The Tale of Christopher Columbus

The New ValueTales® Series Created by
Spencer Johnson, M.D.
#1 *New York Times, USA Today Bestselling Author*

THE VALUE OF
DEDICATION
14
The Tale of Albert Schweitzer

The New ValueTales® Series Created by
Spencer Johnson, M.D.
#1 *New York Times, USA Today Bestselling Author*

THE VALUE OF
CARING
The Tale of Eleanor Roosevelt

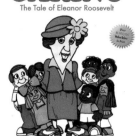

The New ValueTales® Series Created by
Spencer Johnson, M.D.
#1 *New York Times, USA Today Bestselling Author*

THE VALUE OF
RESPONSIBILITY
16
The Tale of Ralph Bunche

The New ValueTales® Series Created by
Spencer Johnson, M.D.
#1 *New York Times, USA Today Bestselling Author*

THE VALUE OF
SAVING
17
The Tale of Benjamin Franklin

The New ValueTales® Series Created by
Spencer Johnson, M.D.
#1 *New York Times, USA Today Bestselling Author*

THE VALUE OF
KINDNESS
18
The Tale of Elizabeth Fry

The New ValueTales® Series Created by
Spencer Johnson, M.D.
#1 *New York Times, USA Today Bestselling Author*

THE VALUE OF
CREATIVITY
19
The Tale of Thomas Edison

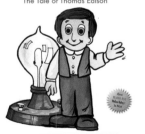

The New ValueTales® Series Created by
Spencer Johnson, M.D.
#1 *New York Times, USA Today Bestselling Author*

THE VALUE OF
TRUTH & TRUST
20
The Tale of Cochise

The New ValueTales® Series Created by
Spencer Johnson, M.D.
#1 *New York Times, USA Today Bestselling Author*

THE VALUE OF
IMAGINATION
21
The Tale of Charles Dickens

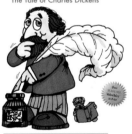

The New ValueTales® Series Created by
Spencer Johnson, M.D.
#1 *New York Times, USA Today Bestselling Author*

THE VALUE OF
FORESIGHT
22
The Tale of Thomas Jefferson

The New ValueTales® Series Created by
Spencer Johnson, M.D.
#1 *New York Times, USA Today Bestselling Author*

THE VALUE OF
DETERMINATION
23
The Tale of Helen Keller

The New ValueTales® Series Created by
Spencer Johnson, M.D.
#1 *New York Times, USA Today Bestselling Author*

THE VALUE OF
GIVING
24
The Tale of Ludwig Van Beethoven

The New ValueTales® Series Created by
Spencer Johnson, M.D.
#1 *New York Times, USA Today Bestselling Author*

GIFT

This Book Is A Gift

For: _____

From: _____

THE VALUE OF
COURAGE

The Tale of Jackie Robinson

For more information about The New ValueTales® visit

www.ValueTales.com

New Text by
Spencer Johnson, M.D.

New Series Enhanced Art by
Emerson Johnson
And A Team of Illustrators and Color Artists

THE VALUE OF
COURAGE

The Tale of Jackie Robinson

The New ValueTales® Series Created and Edited By
Spencer Johnson, M.D.

Based on
Original Text by
Spencer Johnson, M.D.

and
Original illustrations by
Steve Pileggi

VALUE TALES
PUBLISHING

The New ValueTale® Books Are Available At:
http://www.ValueTales.com
1 – 800 – 515 - 0848

Published in the United States of America by ValueTales Publishing.

Volume 4, Edition 1, *The New ValueTales® Series*

Published in 2007 under title: The Value of Courage: The Tale of Jackie Robinson.
First ed. published in 1977 under title: The ValueTale of Jackie Robinson: The Value of Courage.

Library of Congress Control Number: 2007921229

ISBN 978-1-934288-03-0

Personal Values; Historical Figures; Role Models; Juvenile Literature; Fairness; Courage; Athlete.

Manufactured in the United States of America.

WELCOME

This fictional tale is about Jackie Robinson, a real person who lived in California and New York in the 20th century.

The events in this story really happened, and show how useful the value of courage can be. More historical facts are found on page 64.

Now, let's have fun with our story — *The Value of Courage: The Tale of Jackie Robinson* …

ONCE upon a time…

there lived a young boy named Jackie Robinson.

Looking at him you might think he was just an ordinary boy. He walked like his friends. He talked like his friends. He even dressed like his friends.

But there was one thing about Jackie that made him very special. Can you guess what it was?

Jackie could run faster, jump higher, and throw a ball harder than anyone on the block.

"Hey, Jackie! Slow down!" his friends shouted. "We can't keep up with you!"

Jackie laughed. "This is as slow as I can go!" he'd say. Then he would zip off over walls and around fences, running as if his shoes were on fire.

But Jackie didn't have much time for play. His family was poor and Jackie worked to help out his family. He delivered newspapers after school. And on the weekends, Jackie sold hot dogs at a baseball stadium near his home in California.

Jackie worked hard and sold lots of hot dogs. Of course he watched the ball games too, when he got the chance. One day as he watched, Jackie noticed something. It was something he had seen before, but had never really thought about.

He looked at the pitcher and the catcher. He looked at the batter and at the first baseman. He looked at the dugouts where the other players were sitting.

"I don't understand it," he said to himself. "There aren't any black players on either team."

"Hey!" a man shouted. "How about one of those hot dogs?" So, Jackie hurried back to work.

That evening at supper Jackie asked, "Mama, how come black people don't play on big league baseball teams? Aren't they good enough players?"

"Oh, they play well enough, Jackie," his mother answered. "But they aren't allowed to play in the big leagues. Only white men are allowed to play."

His brother Mack poked Jackie in the ribs. He joked, "They're afraid our color might rub off on them." Everyone but Jackie laughed. But at the same time they felt a little sad.

Jackie was angry. "That's not right!" he shouted.

His mother said, "No, I don't suppose it is. But you must control your temper. It's one thing to be brave. It's another thing to have courage."

Jackie didn't really know what that meant — at least not yet anyway. But he knew how he felt.

Jackie felt angry. "If somebody tried to stop me, I'd wrestle him to the ground!" Then he wrestled his favorite brother Mack to the floor to show what he meant.

Jackie's temper often got the better of him when it came to what wasn't right. But his mother understood. "Someday it might change," she said, "but not by fighting with your brother. Now finish your dinner, because I have a surprise for you."

What do you suppose the surprise was?

It was a baseball! Oh, it wasn't the kind of baseball that you can buy in a store.

It was a homemade ragball. Jackie's mother had made it out of woolen socks and bits of brightly colored cloth. She had tied it up with a bit of string and a lot of love.

When Jackie saw that ragball he let out a yell that rattled the windows. "My own baseball!" he shouted happily. "I'll keep it as long as I live!"

After that, whenever he wasn't working or at school, Jackie played with his ragball.

He spent so much time with his ragball, he thought that he and the ball were about as close as peanut butter and jelly.

Sometimes, Jackie would make believe that he was a big league baseball player. He used to hit his ragball with a stick and pretend he was hitting a real baseball with a real bat.

But one day Jackie hit the ragball too hard. It flew up and up and up into the air. And what do you think happened next?

Jackie hit the ball so hard that the ragball split apart. Bits and pieces of colored cloth exploded out of it and scattered everywhere!

Jackie was heartbroken. "I've killed it!" he wept.

But then he thought he heard a strange little voice. "Hello," the voice seemed to say. "My name is Rags." Then he added, "I'm okay! Don't cry, Jackie. I'd like to be your best friend."

Jackie blinked. Suddenly it seemed to him that his ragball was back in one piece, and it was talking to him.

Jackie was smart, so he knew that his ragball was really in little bits and pieces. And it certainly couldn't talk. He was just using his imagination.

He remembered what his mother had said: your best friend is *yourself*. So, when Jackie pretended that he was listening to Rags, he knew that he was really just listening to his own thoughts.

"Well, Rags," Jackie said, "I can't think of a better friend to have."

With that, Jackie went home — and he pretended that Rags went along with him.

As Jackie grew up, he liked to think that Rags went everywhere with him. Rags went along to help him on his jobs. Rags was with him when he practiced his favorite sports.

Sometimes he practiced so much that his whole body ached, but Rags whispered good things to Jackie. "Have courage," he said. "Remember *courage is doing whatever is hard for you to do.*

"And it takes even more courage if you are afraid to do something. When you have courage — and you do what you would do if you were not afraid — nothing can stop you."

"Do you remember the old Pepper Street gang?" asked Rags. Jackie recalled the boys he had known near his home on Pepper Street.

"Remember how hard it was to leave that gang of kids?" he asked. "If you had stayed, you might now be stealing and lying like some of those other kids. Then you'd probably be in big trouble now."

Jackie nodded and said, "It was hard to leave the gang, but I'm glad I was smart enough to leave. I'm a lot happier now."

When Jackie was older he went to college at UCLA — the University of California at Los Angeles — where he became a star athlete. He was the first person in the history of the school to win sports awards in basketball, football, baseball, and track, all in the same year.

"What a great all-around athlete!" said the fans who watched Jackie play.

One person who always rooted for Jackie was a girl named Rachel. Jackie really liked Rachel. He liked her so much that he asked her to be his girlfriend.

Many people cheered for Jackie, but a few tried to bully him because he was black. They called him a troublemaker when he got angry and stood up to them.

"Black people shouldn't talk back." sneered one man.

"I'm a person, just like you," replied Jackie. "And I'll say and do what I think is right!"

Rachel was proud of Jackie when he spoke up this way.

Jackie tried not to worry when people said cruel things to him. He had more serious problems. "I'm going to have to quit school," he told Rags one day.

"Quit school?" cried Rags. "You can't! It's too important!"

"I know, but my family just can't afford to keep me in school," said Jackie. "I have to get a job."

If *you* were a terrific athlete like Jackie, what kind of job would you get?

You would probably get a job playing sports.

Jackie began to make money when he started to play professional football. He was a very, very good player. But he didn't stay with the football team long.

Jackie quit football in order to join the army. Jackie didn't want to, but he did it because he believed he could help his country.

He was a good soldier, but he found some things were wrong, even in the army. One day when he wanted to ride on a bus, he found out how unkind some people could be. Something happened that was very common in those days.

Do you have any idea what it was?

When Jackie got on the bus and sat down, the bus driver yelled at him. "Hey, get to the back of the bus where you belong!"

"I will not," said Jackie. "I'll sit up front just like anybody else." Jackie stayed in the front of the bus.

Some of the passengers did not like this. They felt that only white people were good enough to sit up front. They even tried to get Jackie in trouble. But he had the courage to do what was hard — what he felt was right.

"Atta boy, Jackie!" said Rags. "I'm proud of you!"

Jackie was proud, too. And he was glad when the whole thing finally turned out all right.

But deep down inside, he was sad. He whispered to Rags, "How can some people be so unjust to other people?"

Then, after Jackie finally got out of the army, he needed a job again. And of course the first thing he thought of was sports.

"Why not try baseball?" said Rags. "They don't allow black athletes to play in the big leagues, but you could play for the Negro American League."

Jackie decided to try it. He went to Kansas City and joined the Monarchs, an all-black baseball team. "If baseball works out," he thought, "Rachel and I can get married soon."

After Jackie had been with the Kansas City Monarchs awhile, people began talking about what an outstanding player he was. Sportswriters began turning out stories about the way he could hit, run, throw and catch.

And, while Jackie was playing so well for the Monarchs, an important man who lived far away was also talking about him.

Who do you think the man might be, and what might he be saying about Jackie?

The man was Branch Rickey, the president of the Brooklyn Dodgers, a famous big league baseball team.

"Lots of black people are darn good athletes," Branch Rickey said to a friend. "It's about time they get a chance to play baseball in the major leagues. And, from what you tell me, Jackie Robinson is a great baseball player. I'm going to ask him to play on one of our try-out baseball teams, the one in Montreal."

Branch Rickey knew he'd be criticized. It took courage, but he sent for Jackie anyway. Soon after Jackie arrived in New York at Mr. Rickey's office, he was asked a difficult question.

"I want to know one thing," he said to Jackie. "Can you play the game, no matter how ugly and mean some people are to you? Will you be able to take it without losing your temper?"

"Mr. Rickey," said Jackie, "are you looking for a black man who's afraid to fight back?"

Branch Rickey shook his head. "No. I'm looking for a ball player with courage — someone who is not afraid of *not* fighting back."

Jackie understood. Some white players would do anything to prove that blacks weren't good enough. They would throw baseballs at him, step on him with spiked shoes, and call him ugly names. If he fought back, he could ruin the chances of other black athletes. He just needed to concentrate on playing great baseball in the big leagues.

"It will be hard, so it will take a lot of courage," Mr. Rickey warned. Jackie said he would try. Then he and Branch Rickey shook hands.

Branch Rickey asked, "Jackie, do you have a girlfriend?"

"I sure do," said Jackie. "Her name is Rachel, and she's a great girl."

"Good," said Mr. Rickey. "A great girl is hard to find, and you're going to need all the help you can get."

"We plan to get married as soon as we can," said Jackie.

So Jackie and Rachel were married. Rags was so happy he smiled a big smile. And Jackie was glad to have Rachel and her warmth and wisdom with him when he left for his first game in Montreal.

When Jackie arrived in Montreal, he asked Rags, "What if I don't play well enough? This is just a try-out team. If I'm not good enough I won't get to New York and I won't play for the Brooklyn Dodgers."

"You're as good as any player here," said Rags.

"But I've got to be *better* than any player here," said Jackie.

Rags laughed, "Then be better!" That made Jackie laugh too.

Jackie *was* better!

He hit the ball hard. He caught the ball practically every time. He ran so fast that he even stole a few bases.

And he didn't pay any attention when some players on other teams yelled at him and called him dirty names.

Then, one day the players on another team did something awful!

They threw a black cat out onto the playing field and yelled, "Hey! Jackie Robinson! Here's your cousin! He's black too!"

Jackie's stomach tightened up. His fists clenched. He wanted to fight.

"Careful!" whispered Rags. "You know what Mr. Rickey told you. And remember what your mother said long ago. It's one thing to be brave and to be willing to fight back. But it's another thing to be stronger — to have courage to do what's hard and not fight back."

Jackie thought for a minute, then he did the thing that was so difficult for him to do. He calmed down and refused to fight.

The other men were disappointed when they saw that they couldn't make Jackie lose his temper. They knew if Jackie stayed calm, he would play even better — against them!

He did play better. In fact, he played so well that, after only one year with the Montreal team, Branch Rickey called him and said, "I want you and Rachel to come to New York. You're going to play for the Brooklyn Dodgers."

Yes! Those were the words Jackie had been waiting to hear. He wanted to tell Rachel the good news right away, but was a little worried. "I wonder," he said to Rags, "what will happen to me in New York?"

One of the first things that happened was that many people in New York saw Jackie's picture in their newspapers. In those days, even some of the sportswriters believed that there wasn't a black man in the country who was good enough for the big leagues. "Jackie Robinson will fail," said some of the newspaper reporters.

Jackie sighed. "How can I play well, when so many people want me to fail just because I'm black?"

But before he knew it, Jackie was in a Dodger uniform, ready for his first big league game.

The first game was about to begin. The Dodgers came onto the field to warm up. Jackie tossed a grounder to a famous player named Pee Wee Reese, the great Dodger shortstop.

Pee Wee scooped up the ball and flipped it to Eddie Stanky, the second baseman. Eddie then threw the ball to Jackie. Jackie felt the ball thump into his glove.

It was a simple catch, but a trickle of sweat rolled down the back of Jackie's neck. His heart beat faster, and his hand felt damp inside his glove. Jackie knew that his palms were sweating. He was very nervous for his first big league game!

Then he heard ugly words. "Hey, black boy!" someone shouted. "You don't belong here. Get off the field!"

"So you're Jackie Robinson," someone from the other team yelled. "We'll show you that you can't play in the big leagues."

Jackie's teammates just watched and listened. They didn't try to defend Jackie, even though he was on their team.

Somehow Jackie managed to ignore the shouts and the insults. He played all right when the game finally started. And for a few more games he played very well. But then it happened!

During one very badly played game, some of the angry fans' boos and shouts got too loud for Jackie. Things were getting too hard for him.

Like many people do sometimes, Jackie Robinson lost his courage. He didn't like to admit it, but he was giving up. He began to play worse. In game after game, he failed to hit the ball.

"See!" said one of the players on the other team. "I told you black people aren't any good at baseball!"

Jackie walked sadly back to the dugout and sat there. "Everybody seems to be against me," he sighed. "I feel all alone."

"I know it's hard to do well, Jackie, when you feel all alone," whispered Rags, "but having courage means doing what is hard. Keep on going. Do what is hard. You never know what might happen."

The next game began badly, again. Fans shouted at Jackie. Players on the other team yelled insults. As usual, the men on Jackie's team did nothing to help Jackie.

But then a very unexpected thing happened. Almost everyone in the stadium saw it. The great Dodger player, Pee Wee Reese, walked over, put his arm around Jackie's shoulder, and said, "We're with you, Jackie." He knew how hard it was for Jackie to be the only black player in the major leagues.

At last Jackie had found a real teammate. Now he was more determined than ever to play his best — no matter how hard it was.

Jackie came to bat. The pitcher threw the ball. An instant later the stadium echoed to the sound of a loud crack! Jackie had hit the ball into the outfield for a double!

Jackie played well for the rest of the day — and for many days after that. Gradually most of the fans and players stopped booing and insulting him. They began to admire the way he played.

There was, however, at least one player who still wanted to hurt Jackie. And he planned to do it soon.

During the next game, a big player from the other team charged into second base at Jackie like a wild bull. He cut Jackie on purpose with his spiked shoes. Jackie began to bleed.

Without thinking, Jackie Robinson clenched his fists, ready to fight.

"No," screamed Rags. "That would be too easy. It's what he wants you to do."

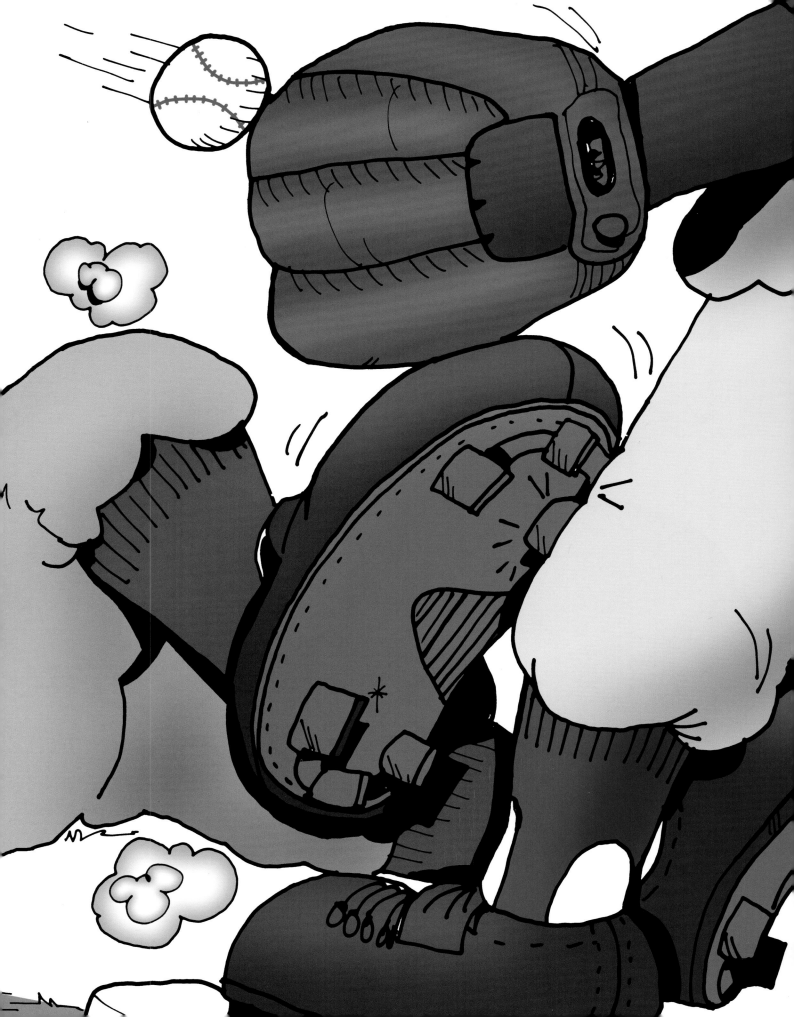

Jackie took a deep breath and relaxed his hands. Soon he was surrounded by many of his teammates, who helped him as he limped off the field.

His teammates knew, and even the fans who read the newspapers knew, that it was Jackie's nature to fight back. It must have been hard and taken a lot of courage for Jackie not to hit the other player.

"Jackie's done it," Mr. Rickey told Rachel. "He's shown he's got great courage when it's needed most."

Rachel couldn't know it that day, but Jackie's courage was going to change baseball completely. And Rachel was going to see the change with her own eyes.

What do you think Rachel saw?

As time went by, Rachel saw more and more black athletes on big league playing fields.

Now everyone knew that a good player was a valuable addition to any team, whether black or white, and especially if they were courageous.

Jackie's courage had led the way and he was able to share what he had accomplished with others!

Rags was so proud that he hardly knew what to do with himself. "Jackie," he said, "you've helped all black athletes, and you've won just about every major award a baseball player can win!"

Jackie laughed. "I know. But I'm happiest because I helped the Brooklyn Dodgers win their first championship of the world."

Jackie grew older and eventually gave up playing baseball.

What do you think he did next?

Jackie Robinson became a leading spokesman for the rights of black people. He talked to groups of people all over the country.

"It's time everyone treated black people as equals," Jackie said. "I know that things are getting a little better, but they need to get much better — and soon!"

Some people didn't want to think about how they treated black people, but Jackie encouraged them to do so. And when they did, some people changed.

Because Jackie had the courage to say what was right, many people admired him. And they became more courageous themselves. Rags was happy for Jackie.

He didn't know it yet, but one of the happiest days for Jackie was yet to come.

One day, Jackie was voted into the Baseball Hall of Fame — the highest honor a baseball player can receive. Some of the greatest baseball players and the country's highest leaders were there to honor Jackie.

As he listened to them cheering, Jackie's eyes filled with happy tears. Rags said, "You've earned this because of your courage. We both know you have courage on your own. So, I will be leaving soon."

People couldn't see it, but Jackie smiled inside and whispered, "Thank you, Rags, for everything. I will always keep you in my heart."

And with that, Jackie nodded a fond goodbye as Rags disappeared.

And now, as our story nears its end, what do *you* think?

Is there something that's hard for you to do? Maybe it's even something that you're afraid of. Are you going to have courage and do it?

What you may want to do in your own life may be different from Jackie Robinson. You can choose whatever you want for yourself.

Whatever you choose, you may find that when you have courage, in big and small ways, you can be happier too — just like our friend Jackie Robinson.

And then, perhaps you can help make the world a little better place by sharing what you discover with others!

The End

DISCUSSION

Now that you know about *The Value of Courage: The Tale of Jackie Robinson* —

What do *you* think?

⭐ Did Jackie Robinson often have the courage to do and say what he thought was right?

⭐ How did Jackie Robinson feel when he forget to use his courage?

⭐ What do you think would have happened if Jackie Robinson had not usually been courageous?

⭐ How do you feel when you have courage and do what is hard for you to do?

⭐ How could you use *The Value of Courage* in your own life?

HISTORICAL FACTS
JACKIE ROBINSON
1919-1972

John Roosevelt (Jackie) Robinson was born in Cairo, Georgia in 1919, the youngest of five children. His sharecropper father abandoned the family six months after Jackie was born. Despite a lack of money, Jackie's mother was determined to find a better life for her children and moved her family to California when Jackie was only sixteen months old.

Jackie and his brothers Edgar, Frank, and Mack, and his sister Willa Mae, grew up on Pepper Street in Pasadena, California. Their mother Mallie supported the family by working at various domestic jobs. Jackie remembered his mother with pride: "I thought she must have some kind of magic to be able to do all the things she did, to work so hard and never complain and to make us all feel happy."

At one point in his youth, Jackie began to run with a neighborhood gang. An older friend made Jackie realize how much he was hurting his mother as well as himself. As Jackie later said, "He told me that it didn't take guts to follow the crowd, that courage and intelligence lay in being willing to be different." Jackie listened and left the gang.

As he grew up, Jackie developed into a sensational athlete. He starred in football, basketball, baseball, and track. He attended UCLA where he became the first person ever to win athletic awards (letters) in all four sports.

Jackie left UCLA in 1941 and began playing professional football with the Los Angeles Bulldogs. World War II cut short his football career. He served in the army for thirty-one months and was discharged as a first lieutenant.

He made his professional baseball debut in 1945 with the Monarchs of the Negro American Baseball League. His abilities as a player brought him to the attention of Branch Rickey, president of the Brooklyn Dodgers baseball team. Rickey, in what was an act of great courage at the time, had decided to break the color barrier which then existed in major league baseball.

Jackie was signed to play for the Dodgers' top minor league team, the Montreal Royals, for the 1946 season.

In 1947 Rickey moved Jackie to the Dodgers. Despite the tremendous pressure of being the first black baseball player in the major leagues, Jackie played outstanding baseball and was voted rookie of the year. His best year was 1949 when he led the league in hitting and was voted most valuable player. Jackie played for the Dodgers for ten years during which they won the National League title six times. In 1955 it was Jackie's spectacular play that led to the Dodgers' first World Series Championship. He retired from baseball after the 1956 season.

Jackie, even as a young person, was an outspoken black man. He was in many ways ahead of his times. Many people did not like his comments on racial injustice. However, he had the courage to speak his mind in public on what he believed to be the rights of blacks.

Jackie shared the pains and joys of his life with his wife Rachel, whom he married in 1946. Rachel was a source of considerable strength for him.

In later life Jackie Robinson suffered quietly from the pain of diabetes. He died from diabetic complications in 1972. But even now his life story continues to act as an outstanding example of the value of courage.

We Hope You Enjoy All The Stories In
THE NEW VALUETALES® SERIES

The New ValueTales® Series is available exclusively at:
www.ValueTales.com

THE VALUE OF BELIEVING IN YOURSELF
The Tale of Louis Pasteur

The New ValueTales® Series Created by
Spencer Johnson, M.D.
#1 New York Times, USA Today Bestselling Author

THE VALUE OF HONESTY
The Tale of Confucius

The New ValueTales® Series Created by
Spencer Johnson, M.D.
#1 New York Times, USA Today Bestselling Author

THE VALUE OF FAIRNESS
The Tale of Nellie Bly

The New ValueTales® Series Created by
Spencer Johnson, M.D.
#1 New York Times, USA Today Bestselling Author

THE VALUE OF COURAGE
The Tale of Jackie Robinson

The New ValueTales® Series Created by
Spencer Johnson, M.D.
#1 New York Times, USA Today Bestselling Author

THE VALUE OF SHARING
The Tale of the Mayo Brothers
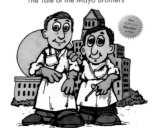
The New ValueTales® Series Created by
Spencer Johnson, M.D.
#1 New York Times, USA Today Bestselling Author

THE VALUE OF HUMOR
The Tale of Will Rogers

The New ValueTales® Series Created by
Spencer Johnson, M.D.
#1 New York Times, USA Today Bestselling Author

THE VALUE OF LEARNING
The Tale of Marie Curie

The New ValueTales® Series Created by
Spencer Johnson, M.D.
#1 New York Times, USA Today Bestselling Author

THE VALUE OF HELPING
The Tale of Harriet Tubman

The New ValueTales® Series Created by
Spencer Johnson, M.D.
#1 New York Times, USA Today Bestselling Author

THE VALUE OF UNDERSTANDING
The Tale of Margaret Mead

The New ValueTales® Series Created by
Spencer Johnson, M.D.
#1 New York Times, USA Today Bestselling Author

THE VALUE OF PATIENCE
The Tale of the Wright Brothers

The New ValueTales® Series Created by
Spencer Johnson, M.D.
#1 New York Times, USA Today Bestselling Author

THE VALUE OF RESPECT
The Tale of Abraham Lincoln

The New ValueTales® Series Created by
Spencer Johnson, M.D.
#1 New York Times, USA Today Bestselling Author

THE VALUE OF FRIENDSHIP
The Tale of Jane Adams

The New ValueTales® Series Created by
Spencer Johnson, M.D.
#1 New York Times, USA Today Bestselling Author